Time for Lunch!

Paul Shipton
Illustrated by Trevor Dunton

One day, Pip was walking home from the library.

A fox was following her, but she wasn't scared.

Pip wasn't big or strong, but she was a clever little chick.

Suddenly, the fox jumped out.
"How are you, little chick?" he said.
"I'm fine, thank you," said Pip.
"No, you're not," snarled the fox.
"I'm going to eat you for my lunch."

The fox licked his lips and opened his mouth wide.

"Wait!" shouted Pip. "You can't eat a chick for lunch without bread."

"Can't I?" said the fox.

"No. It says so in my book," said Pip.

The fox thought about this. He did like sandwiches.

"I'll get some bread," he said. "Wait here!"
He started to run to the farmer's house.
Then he stopped.

"You can't trick me," he said. "I'm taking you with me."

The fox went to the farmer's house and took some bread.

"Time for lunch!" said the fox.

"Wait!" shouted Pip. "You can't eat a chick sandwich without salt."

"Can't I?" said the fox.

"No. It says so in my book," said Pip.

The fox thought about this. He did like
salt on his sandwiches.
"I'll get some salt," he said.

The fox took some salt from the farmer's house.
He put it on his sandwich.

"Time for lunch!" said the fox.
"Wait!" shouted Pip. "You can't eat a
chick sandwich without pepper."
"Why not?" asked the fox.
"It says so in my book," said Pip.

The fox thought about this. He was **very** hungry, but he did want his lunch to be the best.

"I'll get some pepper," he said.

The fox took some pepper from the farmer's house.

"You need lots and lots of pepper,"
said Pip. "It says so in my book."
The fox puts lots and lots of pepper on his
sandwich. He licked his lips, opened his
mouth wide and . . .

He sneezed the biggest sneeze ever!
The sneeze was so big that it blew Pip
up into a tree.

14

The sneeze was so loud that the farmer
heard it.
He was very angry when he saw the
fox on his farm.

Pip climbed down from the tree and went home.

"Did you get a good book?" asked her mum.

"Yes, very good," said Pip.